A Fresh Approach
to Piano Sight-Reading

Joining the Dots

Book 3

Alan Bullard

ABRSM

To the Teacher

Joining the Dots offers lots of material to help build your pupil's skill and confidence in sight-reading. Used as part of regular lessons and practice, it will help students learn to read new music more quickly and easily, developing their awareness of keyboard geography, their sense of key and other general musicianship skills.

The five books in the series cover the keys found in ABRSM's sight-reading tests at each of Grades 1–5, with a section for each key. Each section begins with warm-up and technical material ('Key Features' and/or 'Workouts'), followed by opportunities for improvisation ('Make Music') and several short pieces to sight-read ('Read and Play').

Key Features are a supplement to scales and arpeggios, and will help the pupil to establish basic hand shapes and the 'feel' of each new key under the fingers. They are provided here for those keys not found in Book 1 or 2 and can be practised at various speeds and dynamics, and with different articulations.

Workouts are for exercising and warming up the fingers and hands in the key, and explore a range of techniques. The first of each pair is the same throughout (transposed for each key), to help reinforce key familiarity, while the second is always different.

Make Music provides an opportunity for your pupil to build confidence in (and through) creative and imaginative work, encouraging familiarity with the 'feel' of the key using an approach that is not primarily notation-based. For those keys not found in Book 1 or 2, pupils can make up a tune to fit the rhythm provided; for the more familiar keys there is a new opportunity for composition and improvisation – continuing a right-hand melody over a given left-hand accompaniment. Each activity is designed to work within a five-finger position, but you may wish to encourage your pupil to try a wider range. Approach the activities together in the way you both find most comfortable: for most pupils this will involve exploring the keyboard with some trial and error – experimenting is a good way to learn here!

Read and Play is the goal of each section – a number of short, characterful pieces, to be played at sight or after a short practice time, with the focus on keeping going. These lead up to and include the technical standard to be found in Grade 3 sight-reading and are a useful source of sight-reading material for those preparing for exams.

Because the material is arranged to be at an equivalent level in each key, your pupil can 'jump in' to any section, using it alongside pieces, scales or arpeggios that are being learnt in that key. Within each section, the books are designed so that pupils learn and play the Key Features (where provided) and Workouts before moving on to the Make Music and Read and Play material. The suggested fingerings should work for most players, but are a recommendation only.

Towards the end of the book you will find **More Pieces to Play**, including longer solo pieces and a duet. These can be used in any way you wish – as additional sight-reading practice or as pieces to learn quickly and play through for fun.

with thanks to Janet for her sound advice, and to her pupils for trying these ideas out

First published in 2010 by ABRSM (Publishing) Ltd, a wholly owned subsidiary of ABRSM
24 Portland Place, London W1B 1LU, United Kingdom

© 2010 by The Associated Board of the Royal Schools of Music

AB 3423

Illustrations by Willie Ryan, www.illustrationweb.com/willieryan
Book design and cover by www.adamhaystudio.com
Music and text origination by Barnes Music Engraving Ltd
Printed in England by Halstan & Co. Ltd, Amersham, Bucks.

Dear Pianist,

Joining the Dots will help you to learn new music more quickly and easily.

In this book you will find a section for each key that you are likely to use.

In each section there are several different things to do:

Key Features to get you used to playing in the new keys

Make Music in which you can develop and explore musical ideas

Workouts to exercise your fingers and hands

Read and Play where there are a number of short pieces to play – read the title, work out the rhythm, find the notes and, when you're ready, play the piece right through without stopping!

Towards the end of the book you'll find **More Pieces to Play**, including some longer pieces and a duet for you to play with a friend.

Enjoy Joining the Dots!

Alan Bullard

Workouts

- Use these to warm up in the key of C major

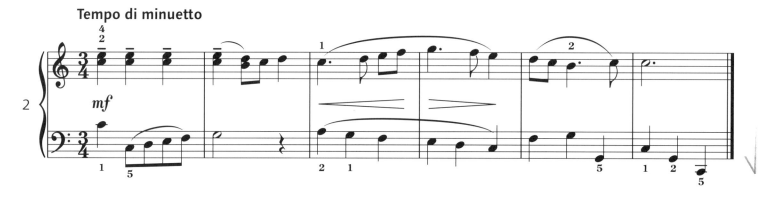

Make Music

Bugle Call

- Play the left hand on its own first
- Then make up a piece in the key of C major by adding your own continuation of the right-hand melody

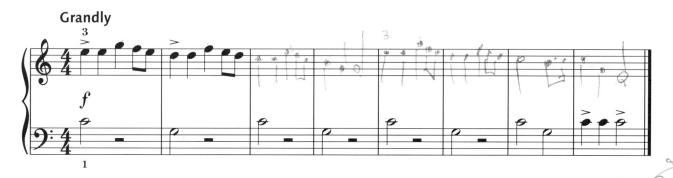

Read and Play

- Prepare carefully, looking out for changes in hand position
- If you like, take a moment to try out the piece
- Finally, play it right through without stopping!

In the Lift

Moderato

Carefree

Jauntily

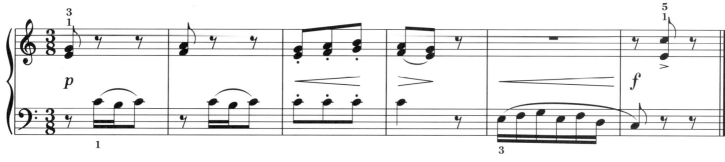

Scherzo

Allegretto

5

Workouts

• Use these to warm up in the key of A minor

Make Music

Gliding

• Play the left hand on its own first
• Then make up a piece in the key of A minor by adding your own continuation
  of the right-hand melody

Read and Play

- Prepare carefully, looking out for changes in hand position
- If you like, take a moment to try out the piece
- Finally, play it right through without stopping!

Far Out to Sea

The Bee

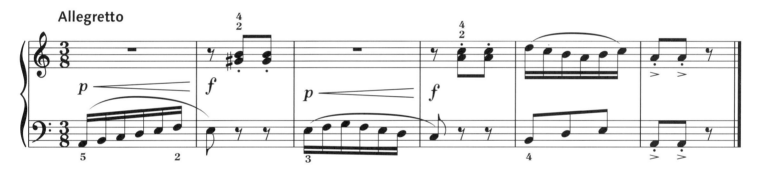

Russian Dance

G major

Workouts

- Use these to warm up in the key of G major

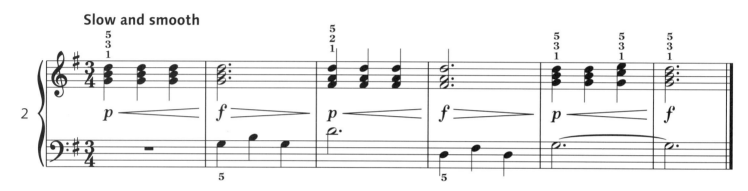

Make Music

Approaching Pipers

- Play the left hand on its own first
- Then make up a piece in the key of G major by adding your own continuation of the right-hand melody

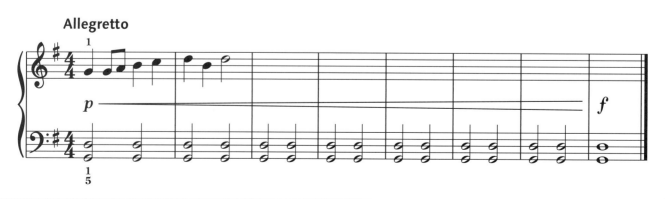

Read and Play

- Prepare carefully, looking out for changes in hand position
- If you like, take a moment to try out the piece
- Finally, play it right through without stopping!

Toodle-oodle-oo

Footsteps

Spring Song

E minor

Workouts

- Use these to warm up in the key of E minor

Make Music

Far Away

- Play the left hand on its own first
- Then make up a piece in the key of E minor by adding your own continuation of the right-hand melody

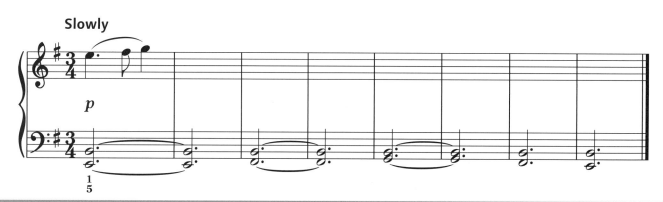

10

Read and Play

- Prepare carefully, looking out for changes in hand position
- If you like, take a moment to try out the piece
- Finally, play it right through without stopping!

Morning Exercise

Allegro non troppo

Journey's End

Andante mesto

Funfair

Lively

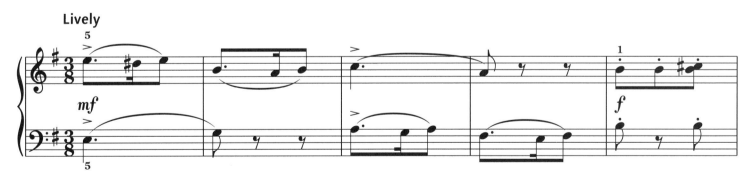

F major

Workouts

- Use these to warm up in the key of F major

Allegretto ritmico (quavers may be swung ♩ = ⌐♪)

1

Moderato

2

Make Music

Alarm

- Play the left hand on its own first, counting the rests carefully
- Then make up a piece in the key of F major by filling in the gaps in the right-hand part

Allegretto

Read and Play

- Prepare carefully, looking out for changes in hand position
- If you like, take a moment to try out the piece
- Finally, play it right through without stopping!

Times Past

The Shadows Lengthen…

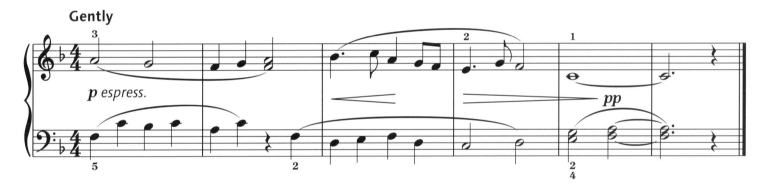

Sunny Morning

D minor

Workouts

• Use these to warm up in the key of D minor

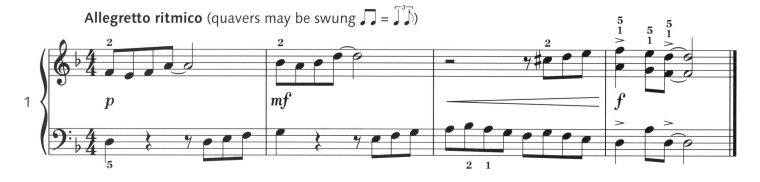

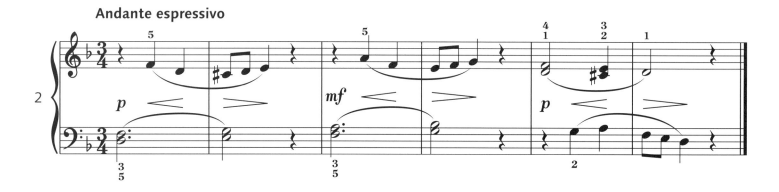

Make Music

The Old Farmhouse

• Play the left hand on its own first
• Then make up a piece in the key of D minor by adding your own continuation of the right-hand melody

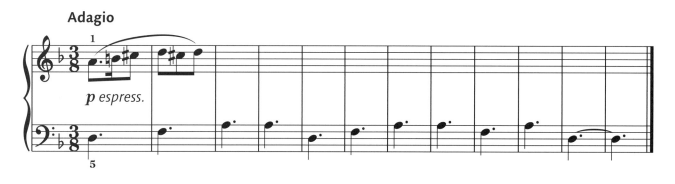

Read and Play

- Prepare carefully, looking out for changes in hand position
- If you like, take a moment to try out the piece
- Finally, play it right through without stopping!

Who's at the Door?

Interrupted Conversation

Mr Mystery

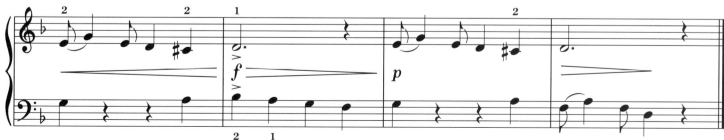

D major

Workouts

- Use these to warm up in the key of D major

Make Music

A Step in Time

- Play the left hand on its own first
- Then make up a piece in the key of D major by adding your own continuation of the right-hand melody

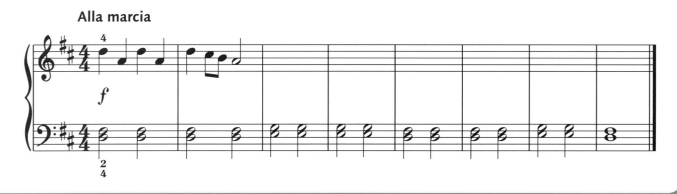

Read and Play

- Prepare carefully, looking out for changes in hand position
- If you like, take a moment to try out the piece
- Finally, play it right through without stopping!

Trumpet Tune

Maestoso

Green Meadows

Gracefully

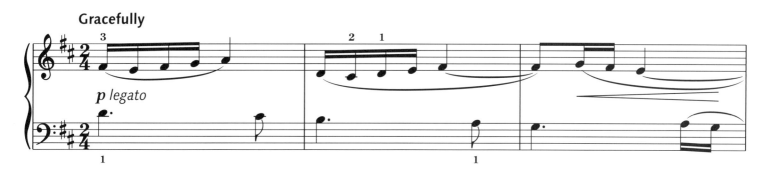

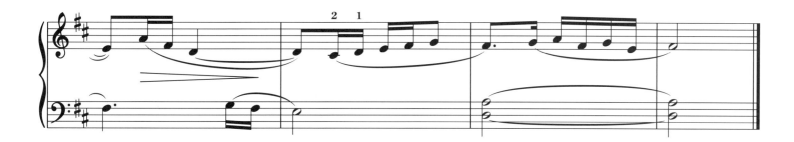

Wandering

Andante

B minor

Key Features

- Play these with each hand separately
- Practise each pattern smoothly and detached, and loudly and quietly

Workouts

- Use these to warm up in the key of B minor

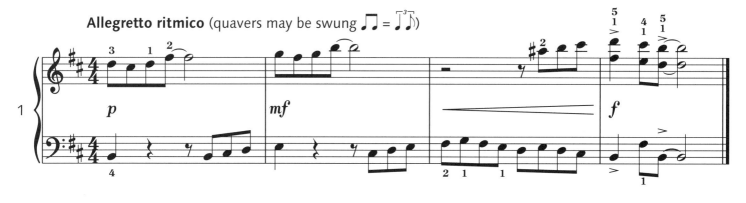

Make Music

Falling Rain

- Tap this rhythm several times
- Then make it into a melody in the key of B minor (using either hand)
- Finish on the note B

Gently

Read and Play

- Prepare carefully, looking out for changes in hand position
- If you like, take a moment to try out the piece
- Finally, play it right through without stopping!

Miniature Minuet

Tempo di minuetto

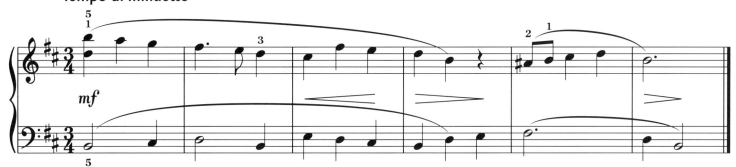

Wandering Wizard

Steady and rhythmic

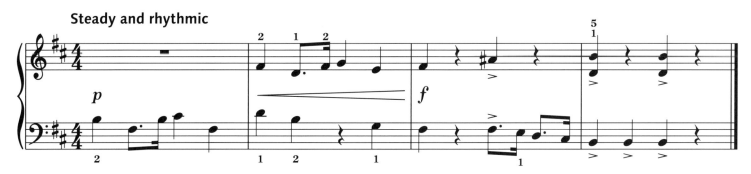

B minor

Story from the Past

Figure in the Shadows

Interrupted March

Key Features

- Play these with each hand separately
- Practise each pattern smoothly and detached, and loudly and quietly

Workouts

- Use these to warm up in the key of Bb major

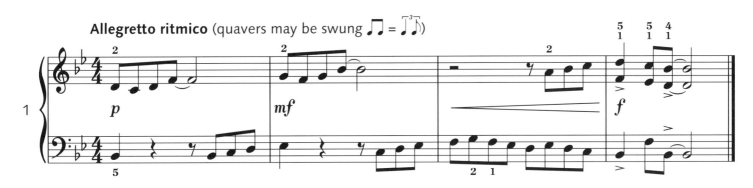

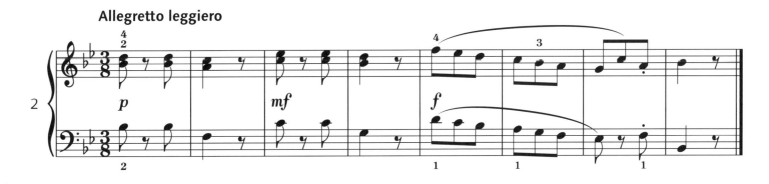

Bᵇ major

Make Music

Climbing High

- Tap this rhythm several times
- Then make it into a melody in the key of Bb major (using either hand)
- Finish on the note Bb

Rhythmically

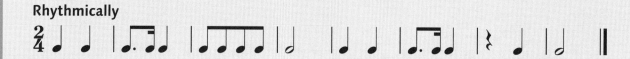

Read and Play

- Prepare carefully, looking out for changes in hand position
- If you like, take a moment to try out the piece
- Finally, play it right through without stopping!

Round the Block

Ronnie's Rag

Echoes of Spring

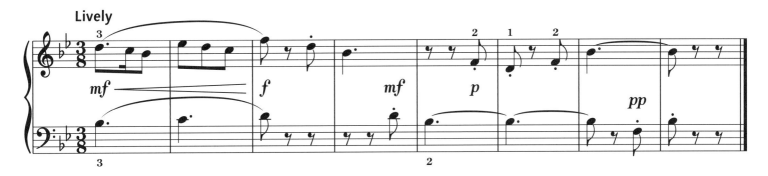

Ripples in the Lake

Out of my Way!

G minor

Workouts

- Use these to warm up in the key of G minor

1

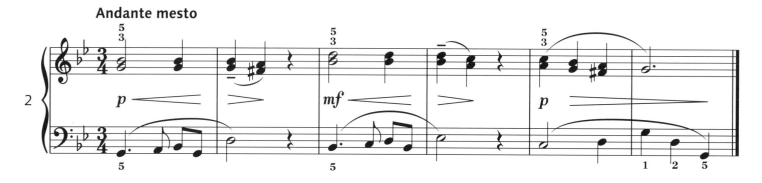

2

Make Music

The Trees are Bare

- Play the left hand on its own first
- Then make up a piece in the key of G minor by adding your own continuation of the right-hand melody

Read and Play

- Prepare carefully, looking out for changes in hand position
- If you like, take a moment to try out the piece
- Finally, play it right through without stopping!

Piper's Dream

Sadly and expressively

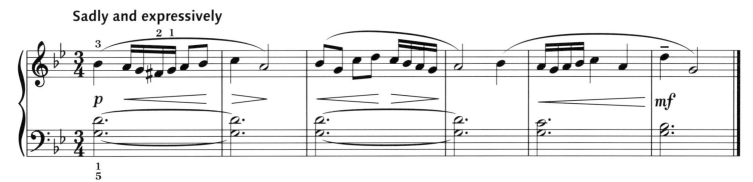

Journey Under Ground

Andante

Taking Flight

Allegro scherzando

A major

Key Features

- Play these with each hand separately
- Practise each pattern smoothly and detached, and loudly and quietly

Workouts

- Use these to warm up in the key of A major

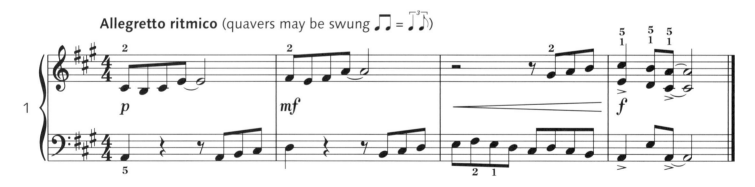

Allegretto ritmico (quavers may be swung ♩♩ = ♩³♪)

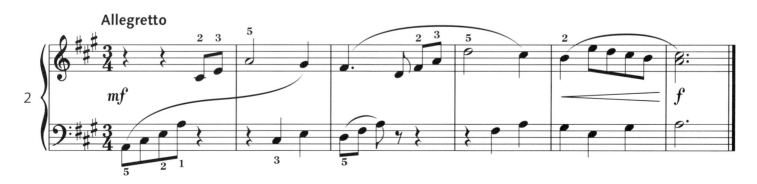

Allegretto

Make Music
May Morning

- Tap this rhythm several times
- Then make it into a melody in the key of A major (using either hand)
- Finish on the note A

Allegretto

Read and Play

- Prepare carefully, looking out for changes in hand position
- If you like, take a moment to try out the piece
- Finally, play it right through without stopping!

Floating Away

Moderato

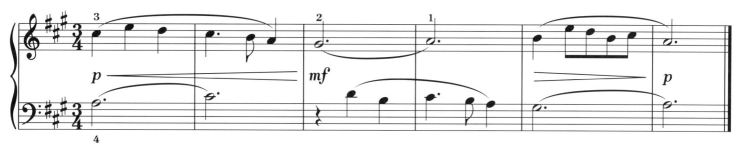

Climbing the Stairs

Alla marcia

A major

Fancy-Free

Happily and jauntily

Jack-in-the-Box

Allegro

Trampoline

Allegretto

Eb major

Key Features

- Play these with each hand separately
- Practise each pattern smoothly and detached, and loudly and quietly

Workouts

- Use these to warm up in the key of Eb major

Allegretto ritmico (quavers may be swung ♩♩ = ♩³♪)

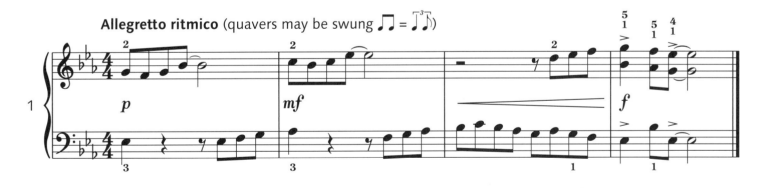

Moderato

Make Music

The Sun Sets...

- Tap this rhythm several times
- Then make it into a melody in the key of E♭ major (using either hand)
- Finish on the note E♭

Andante

Read and Play

- Prepare carefully, looking out for changes in hand position
- If you like, take a moment to try out the piece
- Finally, play it right through without stopping!

Seriously Solemn

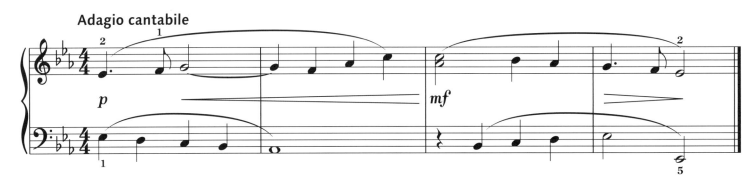

Musical Box

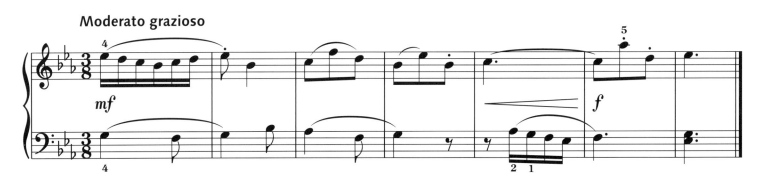

Dialogue

Smoothly

Summer Stroll

Moderato

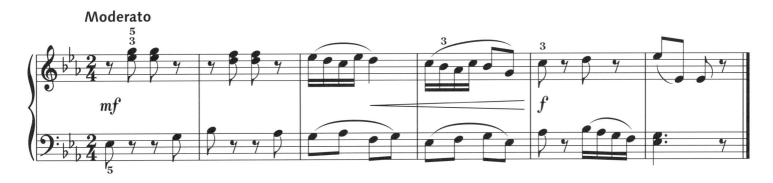

Moonwalk

Exploring gently

More Pieces to Play

- On the remaining pages you will find a variety of pieces of different lengths
- You can use these for playing at sight, or as pieces to learn on your own or with your teacher
- Don't forget to check the key signature and look out for changes in hand position

Snowy Mountains

Jumping in the Pool

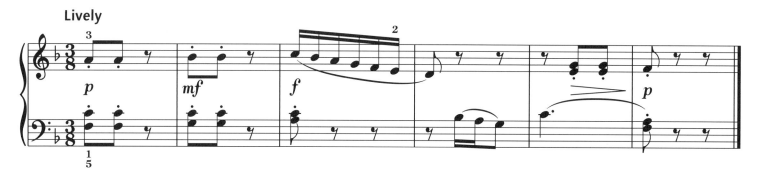

Undercurrents

Crossing the Stream

Cloudy Night

Moderato

Dance Steps

Tempo di valse

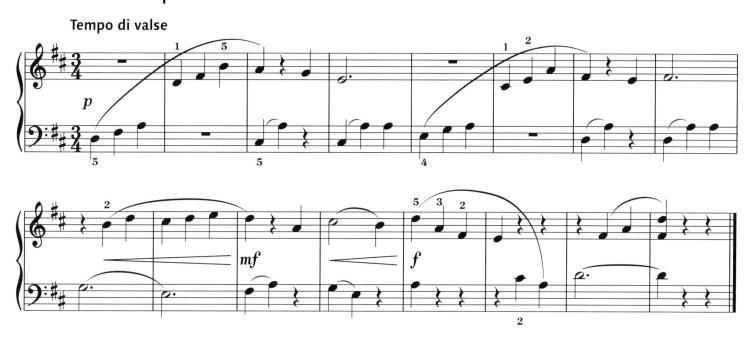

Holiday Mood

With enthusiasm

• Here's a duet to play with a friend

Lost in Thought...

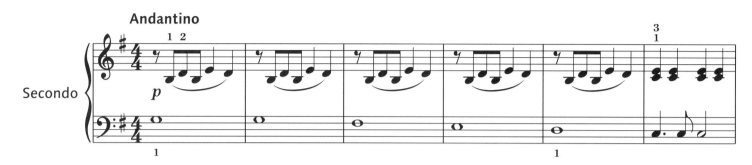

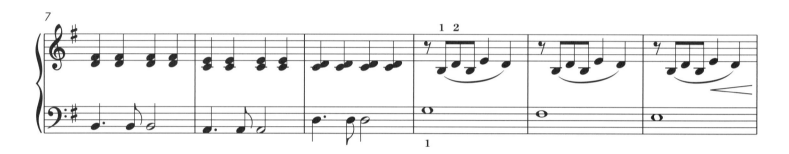

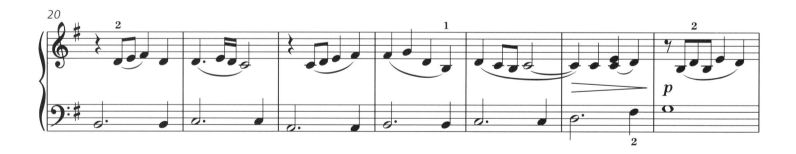

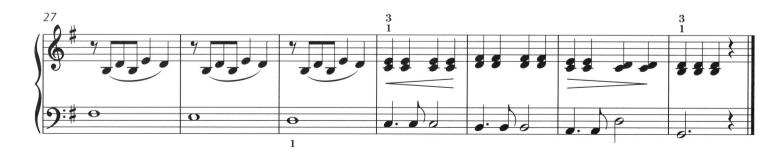

Lost in Thought…

Washing-up Rag